JAZZ MASTERS
Dave Brubeck

Wise Publications
New York/London/Cologne/Sydney

Exclusive distributors:
Music Sales Limited,
78 Newman Street,
London W1P 3LA,
England.

Music Sales Pty. Limited,
27 Clarendon Street,
Artarmon,
Sydney,
NSW 2064,
Australia.

This book © Copyright 1978 by
Wise Publications

Music Editor:
Bob Houston

Text:
Christopher Bird

Cover photographs:
David Redfern, SKR Photo/LFI,

Photographs:
David Redfern, SKR Photo/LFI,
Valerie Wilmer

Art director:
Howard Brown

Designer:
Paul May

ISBN 0.86001-512.2
AM 21189

Music Sales complete catalogue lists thousands
of these and is free from your local music
book shop, or direct from Music Sales Limited.
Please send 30p in stamps for postage to
Music Sales Limited, 78 Newman Street, London W1P 3LA.

Printed in England by
The Camelot Press Limited, Southampton.

Contents

All music by David Brubeck
except 'Take Five' by Paul Desmond

Dave Brubeck

If any should doubt the penetration of Dave Brubeck's music into our popular culture, the sight of that most British of institutions–a colliery brass band–blowing their hearts out on 'Blue Rondo A La Turk' must silence all but the most sceptical. When the magnificent Grimethorpe Colliery Brass Band rattled through 'Blue Rondo'–written by Dave and inspired by one D. Turk, a contemporary of Mozart who has vanished into obscurity except as a one-man obstacle course for aspiring pianists–on television, it's a pity the satellite wasn't used to bounce the picture into Brubeck's California home. He'd have been knocked out.

The Dave Brubeck Quartet was one of the most successful and controversial of jazz groups. When the original quartet first barnstormed through American campuses in the Fifties, its sheer success with an audience fresh to jazz and the subsequent media exposure–the horn-rimmed face of the pianist/leader was granted the US equivalent of a mention in the Queen's honours list, the cover of the national news magazines–was guaranteed to ruffle the feathers of those who felt there was something immoral about this degree of acclaim and financial success for jazzmen. Especially young, white, whipper-snappers from the West Coast.

In retrospect, some eight or nine years after the group's demise (apart from the brief 25th anniversary revival in late 1976), it seems astonishing that Dave's career should have aroused such heated argument, for there was little indication of the furore to follow when the young Brubeck first came to notice as a composer and pianist on the West Coast thirty years ago.

For an international jazz musician and composer, his background is unusual. Born in 1921 in Concord, California, his father was a cattleman and buyer of herd beef and manager of cattle ranches. He always envisaged that Dave would somehow follow in his footsteps and if it hadn't been for his mother–a remarkable woman who somehow managed to become a musician herself and inculcate a love of music in all her children, this may well have happened. His brother Howard, particularly, is now known as a 'straight' composer of some significance and is part of the higher music education system in America.

In an interview which he gave in *Down Beat* in 1957, Dave said, 'It was apparent right from the beginning that I would be a composer. I was always improvising by the time I was four and five and I refused to study! My mother saw this and taught me completely differently from Howard, who is

about the most schooled musician I can think of. At the time when I was very small it was impossible to make me play any of the classical pieces except when I could sit down and play them by ear. So I developed differently from my brothers.'

Although surrounded by music Brubeck embarked on a high school course which was supposed to lead him to become a veterinarian. A perceptive zoology teacher noticed him constantly paying attention to the young musicians practising in the music department instead of listening to him. At the end of the year he simply said,

'Why don't you just go over there? That's where you belong!' And so Dave turned to music full-time; studying by day and working with dance, cowboy and hillbilly bands at night.

In 1942 he joined the army, and even though he was immediately thrust into the company of a large number of extremely competent musicians it seems clear from the stories at the time that most of his own material was far too radical for his contemporaries. He's told a story in the past of how he wrote an arrangement for the army band he was in and nobody would play it; so he took it to Stan Kenton, king of 'progressive' jazz, who simply said 'Bring it back in ten years!'

Later he went to Germany where, after a short bout of service as a rifleman, he was able to get into music again until his discharge in 1946 when he enlisted at Mills College in Oakland in order to study with Darius Milhaud, a leading contemporary composer and a brilliant teacher. So depressed was Brubeck at the reception his music was receiving from his fellow musicians he thought of leaving jazz altogether, the form seeming too narrow to encompass his musical ideas. But, ironically, it was the French composer who convinced him to stay with jazz, arguing that this was the culture he knew best, a vital and

important part of American music.

This was the period when some of us in Britain first heard the name Dave Brubeck, with a series of records on the Fantasy label by his trio, and an octet specially formed to play the music written for the Milhaud classes. It was around this time that Paul Desmond, himself a student at San Francisco College, began to come into the picture, and during the next few years they worked together regularly until finally, in 1951, the Dave Brubeck Quartet was born and that illustrious partnership was finally cemented on a regular basis.

It is important to recall these years because out of them begins to emerge the picture of a kind of musician who is much rarer in jazz than one might like to believe; the total individual. When one thinks that so much is made of jazz as a music of individual self-expression, this may seem odd. But in reality most aspiring jazz musicians are prone to follow the fashions set by the leaders in any given period. In an article in *Crescendo* magazine, written in 1962, Dave's wife, Iola, recalled that when he came back from overseas he found the musical picture drastically changed by Dizzy Gillespie, Charlie Parker and Charlie Mingus who, though not yet the influential figure he was to become, was at that time working on the West Coast with the deep and searching musical ideas that Brubeck admired greatly. His admiration for Gillespie and Parker was great also but when urged by a long-time friend and member of the octet, tenor saxophonist Dave Van Kreidt, to change his style, he replied, 'I like what those guys are doing. I know what they're doing; I understand it. They say it better than anyone else. Let them say it their way. Let me say what I want in *my* way.'

In the two years following the formation of the Quartet Brubeck soared to national importance, with his Fantasy records selling better than any previous jazz albums, his personal appearances in clubs and concerts drawing full houses. This was a time when he made an effort to start playing college concerts–nowadays more commonplace, but at the time a most unusual step–because he sensed that there was an audience there. The success of those early albums, 'Jazz at Oberlin' and 'Jazz at the College of the Pacific' led to his being signed by a major record company, Columbia, and his first two albums for that label, 'Jazz goes to College' and 'Brubeck at Storyville' were enormous hits.

The most successful group of the post-war era was well and truly on its way and with the addition of drummer Joe Morrello sometime in 1956 and, a little later, bassist Gene Wright the group now possessed a far superior rhythm team than any that Brubeck had worked with before; he was ready to explore the world of time more thoroughly than anyone so far in jazz. His reputation as a jazz composer was about to grow enormously.

Even Dave's severest critics–and he has never lacked them–admit to his skill as a composer, but in Brubeck's own opinion improvisation is always the primary factor in the creation of jazz music. In his methods of composition it is likely that he resembles some of the great keyboard improvising composers of the past in that many of his ideas will have first appeared in the white heat of improvisation in the course of live performance.

Maybe one of the reasons for Brubeck's uneven reputation as a performer is that he actually *believes* and tries to put into practice what he says i.e. jazz is about a new performance on each occasion. Contrary to popular belief most jazz musicians actually don't do this but (with the exception of the free improvising school which began to appear in the late Fifties) prefer instead to polish well-tried phrases, runs and arpeggios which fit the comfortable chord sequences. It is clear from listening to many recorded performances and tapes that Brubeck, even

though not always successful, genuinely tries to create new unfamiliar material.

On this point Paul Desmond, who as an improvisor seemed to have no critics, was quite adamant. He once told the American critic Nat Hentoff, 'When Dave is playing at his best it's a profoundly moving thing to experience; emotionally and intellectually. It's completely free, live–improvisation in which you can find all the qualities about music that I love–the vigour and force of simple jazz, the harmonic complexities of Bartok and Milhaud, the form (and much of the dignity) of Bach, and, at times, the lyric romanticism of Rachmaninoff.'

Christopher Bird

Christopher Bird is the journalist *nom-de-plume* of British Musicians' Union organiser Brian Blain. A regular contributor to European jazz publications for more than a decade, he combines his writing with active participation in jazz activities through organisations such as the Jazz Centre Society, of which he was a founder member and moving spirit.

Back To Earth

Blue Rondo A La Turk

18

19

Bluette

1st Improvisation

2nd Improvisation

3rd Improvisation

4th Improvisation

Castilian Blues

1st Improvisation

2nd Improvisation

3rd Improvisation

4th Improvisation

Countdown

2nd Improvisation

3rd Improvisation

Danse Duet

1st Improvisation
Gaily (♩. = 62)

45

Far More Blue

1st Improvisation

2nd Improvisation

3rd Improvisation

Fast Life

2nd Improvisation

It's A Raggy Waltz

1st Improvisation

2nd Improvisation

3rd Improvisation

Pick Up Sticks

The upper note of the bass pattern should be very soft.

The chord of Bb7 is used throughout.

1st Improvisation

2nd Improvisation

70

3rd Improvisation

R.H. rhythm should be gradually changed to equal eighth notes.

Kathy's Waltz

2nd Improvisation

3rd Improvisation

Maori Blues

✱ If the player's hand is small, the lower note of the chords may be omitted.

4th Improvisation

Right Hand 8va on repeat

Take Five

Three's A Crowd

2nd Improvisation

Unsquare Dance

Moderately fast

✽ The hand clapping and drum parts cued in this arrangement are those used by Dave Brubeck and the Quartet in their Columbia recording (CL 1690-CS 8490). They are included in case the pianist may have help from one or two friends in performance. Without such help, the section from A to B may be omitted.

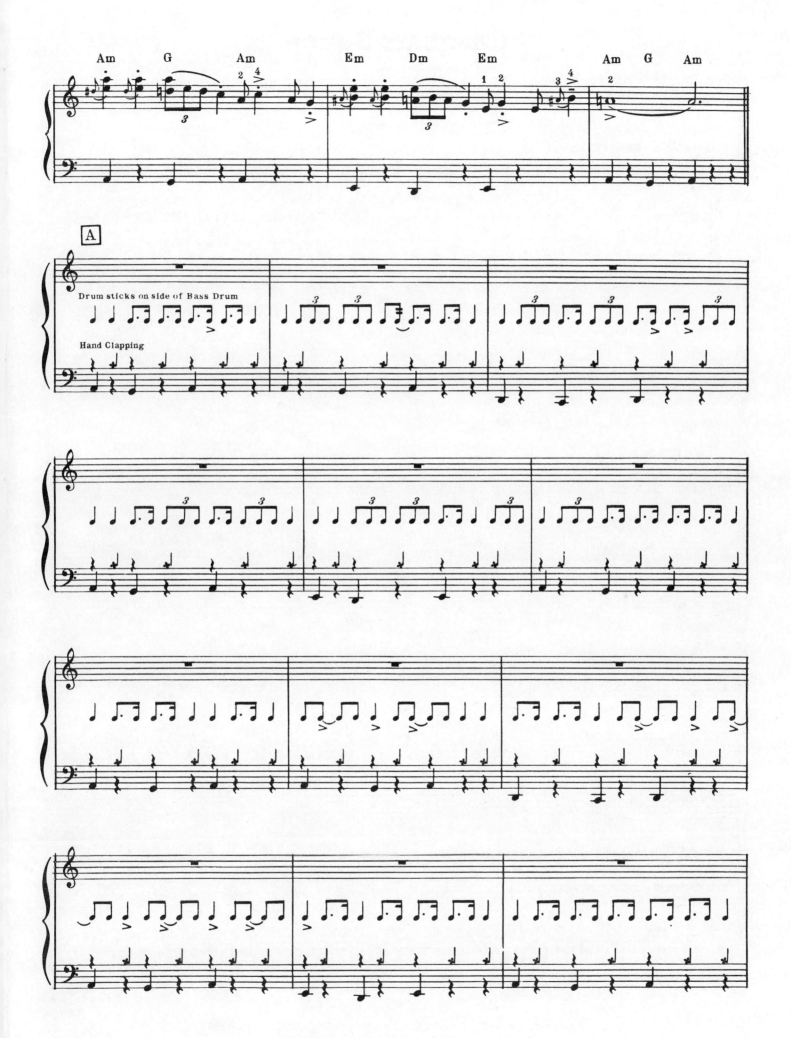